Shakespeare in the Red

Academician
M. S. BAZAGONOV

Shakespeare in the Red

*Tales from Shakespeare
by a Soviet Lamb*

ARC BOOKS, Inc.
New York

Published 1965 by ARC BOOKS, Inc.
219 Park Avenue South, New York, N.Y. 10003
Copyright © Flegon Press, 1964
*All rights reserved, including the right to reproduce
this book, or any part thereof, in any form, without permission
in writing from the publishers.*
Library of Congress Catalog Card Number: 65-23768
Printed in the United States of America

Contents

Foreword

HAVING noticed the distortions in which present-day English and American Shakespearologists are shamelessly indulging, we decided to present in a scientific way some of the best-known plays by William Shakespeare, a truly progressive writer, for the benefit of those of our glorious workers who are so busy building Communism that they have not the necessary time to read them in full.

It is interesting to note that the Great Lenin was a voracious reader of Shakespeare, whose "Complete Works" he always kept by his bedside together with the writings of Marx and Spencer,[1] a point already stressed by us in a previous book entitled *Lenin's Influence on Shakespeare*. Even I. V. Stalin, who, as we all know had made many mistakes for which he is being punished posthumously, was, in his way, an admirer of Shakespeare and particularly enjoyed the mass murders with which some Shakespearian plays end. Naturally, nowadays, when the struggle for peace and freedom is in full swing, Shakespeare has an honoured place in our society.

The following plays, revised and brought up to date

* H. Spencer, English Philosopher (1820-1903)

as Shakespeare himself would have written them if he had enjoyed the freedom of our Soviet writers, are dedicated to the Soviet Working Class because they are, in the words of the famous English writer, "As You like It".

We apologize to our readers for any mistakes in English because although we learned the language from an eminent Soviet Professor who had actually spent over a fortnight in Britain at a Peace Congress and knew the language, as the Russians say, from the horse's mouth, English is not after all our mother tongue.

Academician M. S. BAZAGONOV
Merited Historian
Holder of the Lenin Prize

Macbeth

THE action of the play "Macbeth" takes place in Scotland before that beautiful country had been enslaved by the English colonialists. The present sufferings of the Scottish people, living under the English yoke, are terrible enough, but the oppressed Scots can take heart from the fact that the predatory English Empire is breaking up and after Ghana, Nigeria and Tanganyika, it will certainly be Scotland's turn to become free.

Unfortunately, the turn of the enslaved Welsh people, languishing under the same cruel yoke, will come much later because they are the most underdeveloped tribes of the British Isles, still believing in Druids, a kind of backward witch-doctors, who are actually in the pay of the English imperialists.

But reverting to Scotland, we can rightly say that in spite of such Scottish Quislings as Macmillan, Macleod and Home (the last named being the darling of the English exploiters who call him "Home, Sweet Home"), the brave Scots destest the English invaders. It is no secret that at the present time the Scots are being advised by Dr Nkrumah on how to wage their struggle for independence; this undaunted champion of freedom has managed to smuggle dozens of

Ghanaian agents into Scotland disguised as West Indian immigrants.

At the time of our play, there reigned in Scotland a kindly monarch, King Duncan the Meek, who sought to restrain the rapacious instincts of the Scottish tribal chiefs, who each ruled a clan and savagely fleeced the poor shepherds under their sway. The tribal chiefs were lavishly dressed in strange-looking garments: they wore skirts instead of trousers and had daggers in their stockings, to terrorize the toiling masses of shepherds, whose skirts were growing shorter and shorter and whose shepherd pies—their meagre food—were shrinking every day. Each tribal chief was surrounded by a group of retainers who held an umbrella over his head, to shelter him from the almost unceasing rain. Many of these Scottish chiefs were already in the pay of the English imperialists, who used to bribe them with gifts of extravagant umbrellas.

Scotland is a dangerous country to live in because its lakes, or lochs, are inhabited by man-eating denizens such as the notorious Loch Ness Monster, which still frightens away tourists who venture on its domains, while the English police turn a blind eye to this reign of terror. The Scottish national drink is whisky, a diluted vodka, and their staple food is "haggis", which corresponds in colour to Russian caviare. Hogmanay, Scottish Independence Day, is still celebrated in Scotland in the New Year but its observance is strictly forbidden in the rest of the British Isles, where people are forced to work as usual. But this must end our explanatory notes about Scotland.

At the beginning of our play, we see the victorious

Scottish generals Macbeth and Banquo returning home from the War for the Defence of the Fatherland against the wicked Norwegians, an aggressive people, now of course members of the NATO imperialist alliance. As they were riding along side-saddle (the Scots have to ride in this way because they wear skirts) the generals were discussing military matters of the utmost urgency, such as the demobilization of the armed forces, because the soldiers were badly needed in farming and in such other peaceful pursuits as whisky distillation. Crossing over a blasted heath, the generals noticed three bearded women, shabbily dressed, looking like the beatniks of today, or better still like the twin sisters of Marx and Engels. On account of their uncouth appearance one might have thought them creatures from another planet, but definitely not Venus. Nevertheless, Macbeth and Banquo started up a conversation with them because, even with beards, they were still women and the generals had lived in complete isolation at the front for many months.

"Hello, lassies!" said Macbeth, "What's your names?" And they replied in chorus: "We are the Weird Sisters!" To the generals this sounded very much like some vocal group, so they thought they might be some country-style singers. Then the first bearded woman addressed Macbeth, with a twinkle in her eye: "And how are you, thane of Glamis?" Macbeth quickly glanced at his documents and wondered: "That's right, how could she know?" The second sister said: "And how are you, thane of Cawdor?" "They slipped up that time," murmured Macbeth to Banquo, "this is a title I haven't got!" The third bearded woman croaked: "Hail to Macbeth

11

that shalt be King hereafter!" "It would be very nice, but I don't think so!" mused Macbeth, because in order to be king, Duncan the Meek and his gentle sons would have to die first. Finally, the Weird Sisters addressed Banquo in chorus: "Your heirs will be kings, but not you, laddie!" Then the Weird Sisters mounted broomsticks and vanished on shortwaves; and the generals suddenly realized that they had been having intercourse with witches.

In point of fact, Soviet historians have definitely established that the Weird Sisters were English secret agents, wearing beards as a disguise, and that their mission was to foment civil strife in Scotland through false predictions.

The generals stood pondering on the strangeness of this event for some time until they were roused from their thoughts by the sound of horses' hooves. They perceived in the distance a young man riding a horse inscribed with the letters OHMS, so they gathered that he was a messenger from King Duncan. The messenger dismounted and handed Macbeth a diploma, making him thane of Cawdor, which shows us that the Weird Sisters had some high-placed informers, even in the Scottish Royal Chancellery. "You see, the Weird Sisters were right!" exclaimed Macbeth naïvely, and meditated: "Perhaps they are right about the throne, too!" Then he asked his comrade-in-arms: "Do you really think, Banquo, that your children will be kings?" General Banquo, who had received a more scientific education, replied in sceptical verses: "Oftentimes these ministers of darkness —this Shadow Cabinet—tell us truths in little things, to betray us into deeds of the greatest consequence!"

which, by the way, sums up pretty well the real designs of the English agents.

From that moment on, Macbeth began to covet the Scottish throne but shared his criminal ambitions only with his wife and, to ensure maximum secrecy, only when they were actually in bed. One night, in their pillow-talk, he told her of his meeting with the presumed witches, and that was enough to spur Mrs Macbeth into action. She was an energetic woman and it was she who wore the trousers in the family— if we can use this figure of speech in Scotland where nobody wears any. She told him bluntly: "Listen, Mac (short for Macbeth), there is only one solution! You must kill the King and his sons. Otherwise, it's separate bedrooms for us!" This question of separate bedrooms had cropped up before in their marital life. At one time, Mrs Macbeth in order to punish her husband for insubordination, had retired to a separate bedroom for two long years, meeting her husband only once a week, for the bare minimum. And now, Macbeth was faced with the agonizing choice between committing murder or enduring the torture of a solitary bedroom in the chilly climate of Scotland, in which country wives are the only central heating a man can have.

An opportunity for murder arose soon when King Duncan decided to visit Macbeth Castle, in order to decorate the General for his recent feats of arms. Macbeth Castle was a beautiful modern building for that age, with large banqueting halls and with all medieval conveniences, clearly marked: "Knights" and "Dames".

The King was met by General Macbeth on the draw-bridge (a bridge with forward motions and drawbacks), wearing a gala skirt; and he greeted the King in the traditional Scottish manner, by offering him a tray with a piece of haggis and a glass of whisky. As a present for Mrs Macbeth, the King had brought a rich diamond, beautifully set by a famous Scottish jeweller, McTiffany, selected that very day at breakfast. When he set eyes on Mrs Macbeth, the King bowed politely and said: "I kiss your hand, Madame, and I hope that you are mighty proud of your valiant husband because I am going to decorate him now with the Order of 'Scotland the Brave', First Class, for his heroic deeds against the wicked Norwegians." Mrs Macbeth was so sweet to him that the King could never have guessed as he gazed into her décolleté, when kissing her hand, that down there beat the heart of a viper.

This deceitfulness of Mrs Macbeth went back a long way: when she was a young debutante she had innumerable love-affairs—she was, as the French say, "chargé d'affaires"—but she put on a false front, and was called "The Lass With the Delicate Affair".

The King, fatigued by the journey—he had twice had carriage-trouble during the day—retired early to his bedroom and posted two pages—he had about twenty pages with him—in the corridor to keep vigil. The General and Mrs Macbeth were tossing in their double bed, unable to sleep, firstly because they were unused to going to bed so early, and secondly because their minds were hatching horrible plots. Suddenly Mrs Macbeth threw aside the bedclothes and revealed her ugly intentions: "This is the moment we've been waiting for!" she cried. "Come on, let's do him in!" And she started to pull her husband by the arm. But Macbeth was still wavering: after all, he

14

had just been decorated by the King, and then there was public opinion to consider; and then he was the King's host and Mrs Macbeth his hostess, and it is up to the hostesses to amuse their guests, not to kill them; and so on, until Mrs Macbeth got the wind up. "Look at my breast," she said trying to spur her husband to action, "even if I had a suckling babe, smiling at me there, I would still disconnect him and dash his brains out if I had sworn to do it!" But such fiery exhortations seemed to fall on deaf ears because Macbeth continued to waver. So finally Mrs Macbeth lost confidence in the manly attributes of her husband, and went out herself to kill the King, holding a kitchen knife in her hand. Walking on tiptoe, she slipped into the King's bedroom without being seen by Page 1 or 2, to whom she had previously administered some sleeping pills in their whisky. Nevertheless, she had to be very careful because if she had been seen in the King's bedroom, besides being suspected of murder she could also have been suspected of something worse than murder, because the King was known to possess a spare key to all the chastity belts in his realm, a medieval privilege called "The Keys of the Kingdom". When she was poised to strike him dead with the knife, she had the impression that the King, with his night-cap on, resembled her own father, and so she could not do it. Very upset, she returned to her husband's bedside and explained: "I couldn't kill him, Mac! He looked too much like my own father!" "That's no reason!" replied Macbeth spitefully, "because father-in-law was an unprincipled scoundrel! He cheated me out of your dowry!" Now really furious, he wrenched the kitchen-knife from his wife's hand and, in his night shirt, betook himself to the

King's bedroom with the words: "I'll polish him off!"
With one stroke of the knife he committed the awful
murder, but when he wanted to leave the scene of
the crime he saw daggers flying through the air and
ghosts orbiting around the ceiling, and he remained
nailed to the spot. He could not even say "Amen"
when Page 1 said to Page 2, "Bless You", because the
latter had just sneezed in his sleep. After a while, with
eyes popping out of his head with fright, he returned
to his wife and, shivering, threw away the knife and
went into the bathroom to wash his hands. "It took
you a long time," remarked Mrs Macbeth sarcastic-
ally, "I thought you'd fallen asleep on the job! Have
you smeared the pages with blood so we can pretend
at the trial that they were the murderers? I thought
not! I have to do everything myself!" And full of
anger she embarked on this smear campaign, also leaving beside the pages the incriminating kitchen-knife.

Next morning the murder was discovered, and
Macbeth and his wife feigned much grief, although
they were more grieved by the fact that the two sons
of the late King had fled abroad to England and asked
for political asylum. General Macbeth, being now the
only heir left in the country, was duly proclaimed
King Macbeth I, and thus the predictions of the Weird
Sisters came true.

Subsequently, as Head of State, Macbeth asked
England to extradite the refugee princes (he even offered an exchange of spies), because he claimed that
they were plotting against him by setting up a movement called "Free Scotland", and that they were
releasing inflated hogskins over the Scottish highlands
with anti-Macbeth slogans. The English Government
naturally refused his request, being only too pleased

with a turn of events so promising for their own intervention in Scotland.

The two pages were tried and sentenced to death;
but Scottish public opinion did not believe the official
version of the events, knowing full well that Macbeth
had more to gain from the death of King Duncan that
the poor pages.

Macbeth then remembered another prediction of
the Weird Sisters, namely that the heirs of General
Banquo would one day be Kings of Scotland, and so
he decided as a preventive measure to liquidate the
Banquo family wholesale. He invited General Banquo
and his son to a banquet and hired some professional
thugs to kill them on their way there, reckoning that
this way he would save on the foodstuffs. The assas-
sins succeeded in killing Banquo, but during the fray
his son got away and fled abroad to join the "Free
Scotland" Movement. Although by now a consumate
murdered, Macbeth, as can be seen, was still unlucky
when it came to the liquidation of his enemies' sons.

Banquo, being dead, could not come to the banquet,
where Macbeth was pretending to wait for him and
cracking jokes with his courtiers about the soup getting cold. Suddenly, Macbeth lost his voice and
turned as white as a sheet, because it seemed to him
that Banquo's ghost had just entered the hall and was
pulling his leg, trying to sit in his chair. The Queen
(formerly Mrs Macbeth) noticing this nervous breakdown, called in some male nurses in white overalls
from the special "breakdown service" to tow the King
away, explaining to the guests that His Majesty has
been seized with an old illness.

Such nervous disturbances occurred more and more
often; the ghosts orbited around Macbeth relentlessly

and he saw kitchen-knives floating in the air and flying saucers bearing King Duncan's head. In desperation, Macbeth made an appointment with the Weird Sisters, to tell them about these disturbing symptoms.

The Weird Sisters lived in a luxurious cave, beautifully decorated with "broomsticks motifs" and when he went to see them, they were just decoding a secret message from the English Intelligence Service, starting with the words : "Bubble, bubble, toil and trouble", evidently instructing them to foment civil strife in Scotland. In order to mislead him, the Weird Sisters pretended that they were doing some underground tests in their cave with an elaborate brew called "Consommé Macabre". This was the recipe :

"Place in a huge cauldron two live toads, two minced bats, a whole serpent, the tongue of a certified mad dog, a sliced lizard, the tooth of a wolf to give it strength, the finger of a dead child carefully washed, and a red-hot mummy, all sprinkled liberally with salt and rat-poison. When it comes to the boil, cool the cauldron with either baboon's blood or the blood of a sow which has eaten her young (whichever you happen to have handy in your larder)."

The Weird Sisters then gave Macbeth a long spoon to sup it, and he rather fancied their morbid taste in brews.

Then the Weird Sisters advised Macbeth to lie down on a couch and tell them exactly what ghosts he saw and how often. After some confabulation among themselves they informed him : "Sire, you are a mighty sick man ! You have, evidently, some grave doubts which are preying on your mind. Now, would you like to be treated by us, or by the specialists, 'The High Spirits', our masters, otherwise known as 'The Shadows'? In their case the treatment will be somewhat more expensive, since it involves the use of special apparatus, like the spiritualist table, which is very costly indeed. But since it's you, we can quote you a special price!" "Och!" replied Macbeth, "give me the full treatment! Call in 'The Shadows'!"—which disposes of the rumour that the Scots are parsimonious.

They all sat down at the magic table and solemnly invoked The Shadows, doubtless some quack doctors in league with them. After they landed, the First Spirit told Macbeth to beware of a certain General Macduff, thane of Fife; the Second Spirit assured him that no man born of woman could harm him; while the Third Spirit told him not to worry because he would be defeated only when woods started to move about. "Master Spirits," Macbeth asked them, "would you kindly tell me if Banquo's issue will ever reign in Scotland?"—obviously an issue which preoccupied him intensely; but at this impromptu question The Shadows said: "No comment" and simply vanished, not knowing what to reply, while the Weird Sisters began to croon softly and perform a lascivious Scottish dance called "Strip the Widow", to distract Macbeth's attention. Anyway, Macbeth was pleased and said: "With you, witches one pays the price but one gets the best. Send the bill to my castle!"

But his delight was somewhat abated when he heard on his return, that General Macduff had packed his bagpipes and fled abroad to join the "Free Scotland" Movement. Enraged, Macbeth took revenge on his family, putting his wife and children to the sword.

Such atrocities and purges made the common people hate Macbeth; the more so as Macbeth had developed an accute form of the most terrible disease: the Personality Cult, ordering that his portraits be hung everywhere and a giant statue of his be erected on Ben Nevis. (Ben Nevis and Ben Hur are the highest peaks in Scotland.) As a result, more and more Scots were fleeing abroad and joinging "Free Scotland" although Macbeth had sealed the frontiers and stopped issuing passports.

In the meantime, Macbeth became a widower. That was a very sad blow for him, because the Queen had been the sole partner in his wickedness and in her bosom he found momentary respite from his nervous troubles. And now, alone, with no bosom to turn to, his sole concern were the ghosts and the dreams. All day long he sat gloomily on his throne reading *"The Interpretation of Dreams"*, or other such literary trash, in order to find out the key to the various apparitions which beset his sleeping hours. His illness grew worse and while at first he had ten dreams per hour, now he was having thirty or forty dreams per hour, a nerve-wrecking experience. From time to time, he vowed to cut down his dreams to ten a night, or less, but his will-power was gone. The Weird Sisters had prescribed some pills called "Dream Deterrents" which in his case proved useless. Relying on the assurances given by The Shadows, he dispensed after a time with his security measures, saying to himself: "Why should I worry? No one can defeat me, because who has ever seen a perambulating wood?"

One afternoon in July, when Macbeth was wearing a light Summer skirt and quietly sipping a glass of whisky, a frightened sentry rushed into the throne room, trembling all over: "Sire, a wood is coming towards us!" "What's the matter with you, soldier?" shouted Macbeth, "Leaving your post like this with fairy tales? Go back immediately before I apply the strictures of military law!" "It's true, Sire," pleaded the sentry, "come and see with your own royal eyes!" Intrigued, Macbeth climbed the observation tower of his castle, rubbed his royal eyes and could hardly believe what he saw. Indeed, a wood in battle formation was steadily advancing towards the castle. In reality, they were anti-Macbethist soldiers of the "Free Scotland" Movement, skilfully camouflaged with tree foliage, and a detachment of Free Scottish Girls wearing fig-leaves. Macbeth paid a piper to sound the alarm and, at the head of his host, went into battle against the wood. Hewing right and left at the human trees, he had already destroyed six or seven oaks when he set eyes on the refugee Macduff, disguised as a poplar, who rushed on Macbeth to avenge the murder of his wife and children. "Don't get excited, deserter Macduff, and stop masquerading as a tree," said the King calmly, recognizing him under his foliage, "sorry to disappoint you, but no man born of woman can harm me!" "That lets me out then!" shouted Macduff waving his branches with joy, "I was not born naturally, but my mother was relieved of me by Caesarean section." "Accursed be the man who believes in witches!" explained Macbeth dolefully, "At last my head is clear on this subject!" "Pity you won't have it for long!" replied Macduff and with one masterly stroke cut off Macbeth's head and presented it to the new legitimate King of Scotland, who ordered it to be hung on the wall in the throne room, above the mantelpiece, as a warning to all would-be Scottish traitors.

And so we reach the end of this play much wiser than we were before. We know how to beware of obscurantism and superstition, those hateful remnants of the past, because who can doubt that the witches made Macbeth lose his head? Secondly, we know that national liberation movements can not be stopped, and progressive-minded people all over the world have the sacred duty to tell the English Imperialists

HANDS OFF SCOTLAND!

Romeo and Juliet

SEEING that the West side story of Romeo and Juliet —that of the Imperialist aggressors—has been the only one in circulation for centuries, we have deemed it necessary to publish the East side story—the Socialist one—of the same immortal love.

The action of this sad and passionate play takes place in Verona, Italy, which at that time was being exploited by two rival commercial trusts, Capulet Limited and Montague Incorporated, belonging to the families of the same names. These huge trusts— manufacturing all the conceivable products of the Middle Ages, from spurs to the most complicated chastity belts with ciphers—were waging a commercial war, which brought hatred and strife in its wake. At one point this hatred, akin to a cold war, had reached such a peak that it was impossible for the employees of these groups of companies to meet each other in the streets without exchanging insults or even blows. These hostilities were watched helplessly by the Prince of Verona, an impotent UNO of feudalism. The two trusts, while secretly hatching take-over bids, resorted to all sorts of chicanery: for instance if an employee of Capulet Ltd was making a speech in the "piazza", the Montague hirelings

would jam it with wooden rattles to prevent the in-
habitants of Verona making up their own minds on
the subject. The trusts also had their own armed
guards, who marauded the city—a situation which
gladdened the heart of Count Paris, the descendant
of an old family of armament manufacturers who had
amassed an enormous fortune in the Hundred Years
War. Count Paris was literally rolling in thalers—
medieval currency—by selling swords to the two
camps and cloaks and daggers to their spies. But the
common people of Verona, who followed this feud
of the Capulets and Montagues with a mixture of
revolt and contempt, used to say: "A plague on both
their houses!"

The positive hero of the play is Romeo Montague
who though born the son of a trustman was inspired
by pacifist and progressive ideas. Like many other
advanced youths of his time, he belonged in secret
to the Renaissance Movement, which was abhorred
by the two powerful families as being antagonistic to
their interests. Romeo had tried for a long time to
ease tension in Verona by proposing a Big Three Conference with the participation of Messrs. Capulet and
Montague and the Prince. It was an arduous task and,
for a start, Romeo tried to win over to his idea of
peaceful coexistence the young girls of Verona, whose
minds, according to his way of thinking, were easier
to influence. Another constructive idea of young
Romeo's to create an atmosphere of greater confidence was a plan for the inspection of armaments from
the air, that is, to station inspectors on treetops in the
area of the two camps so that, from their vantage point
on high, they could effectively spot any undue ac-
cumulation of swords and spears. But Mr Capulet, a

stubborn old exploiter, had already rejected the plan with the words: "If I catch an inspector in one of my trees, I'll break his pate with a stone."

Each year, Mr Capulet organized "un ballo in maschera", a fancy-dress ball, at his sumptuous residence, and invitations were extended to all the notabilities figuring in "Who's Who In Verona", with the exception, of course, of the Montague "clan", as he called them. This fancy-dress ball was the highlight of the fashionable season and reputed to be the gayest social event in medieval Italy. In the year of our play, it was meant to be even more resplendent, since it was intended as a "coming-out" party for his young daughter Juliet, who had now reached the marriageable age of fourteen. In the feudal era, girls used to age more rapidly and at fourteen they were not considered Lolitas, as they would be today. Feudalistic mothers had high hopes for their daughters at this social event and used to tell them: "Keep your eyes on the ball!"

And now to the ball! Wealthy and smart girls, in slinky carriages drawn by horses with spruced-up pony tails, were arriving at the Capulet "Palais de Danse". Alert footmen, wearing the dazzling livery of Capulet Ltd, opened the doors of the carriages and helped out the oligarchic females, whose laughter filled the tapestried halls. Romeo, as a Montague, was naturally not invited, but with the help of the ticket touts he had managed to wangle an invitation by paying a few extra thalers. He wanted to be at the ball in order to work on Rosaline, a buxom debutante, whom he had high hopes of converting to peaceful coexistence. But to avoid unpleasantness he had to go incognito, so he went to a theatrical costumier and

25

hired a very effective disguise, with a mask to match; as a result he was so completely unrecognizable that even Mrs Montague, his own mother, could not have spotted him among the revellers.

His first move at the party was to invite Rosaline to dance, but this Veronese beauty pretended that she was tired and wanted to rest for a while, adding as an explanation "my poor feet" or such similar words in Italian. Then Romeo, who was a divine dancer, looked around for another partner and his experienced eye was caught by a charming maiden, blushing intensely under a gorgeous tapestry depicting Adam and Eve. He went straight to her, bowed deeply and said: "May I have the next gavotte, Miss?" And she replied in a maiden speech that would have put a nightingale to shame: "I don't mind!" Reckoning from her reply that she was intelligent as well as beautiful, Romeo immediately decided to convert her to his ideas. The young maiden was none other than Juliet Capulet, the daughter of the host.

They danced one, two, ten gavottes, because Romeo was enjoying her company enormously. As he confessed later: "I could have danced all night!" While dancing cheek to cheek, Romeo whispered tenderly in her delicious ear: "Pretty Mask, what's your attitude to coexistence?" and because Juliet wanted more details before committing herself, he expounded his plan for the easing of tension in Verona, how the warring trusts should give up the cold war and learn to live side by side in peaceful competition: "Look at us," he finally asked her, "isn't jaw-jaw better than war-war?" His passionate arguments and the soundness of his ideas thoroughly convinced Juliet of the need for coexistence. And, at that very moment, their similar political outlook gave birth to a strong love, based on the advanced idea of peaceful coexistence. After gavotting for a long time, Juliet blushingly took leave of Romeo to join an old female Mask, who looked like a more delapidated replica of herself and seemed therefore to be her mother.

Whistling a happy tune, Romeo went up to his friend Mercutio, a man of advanced ideas and slightly older than himself, the Organizer of the Renaissance Movement for the North of Italy. "Dear Mercutio," said Romeo in a tender voice, "did you see the young thing I've been gavotting with all night?" "Which young thing?" asked Mercutio absent-mindedly, "Rosaline?" because he had not watched Romeo, being himself engaged all the time in an absorbing discussion about the Renaissance with a young widow who possessed a big fortune and who could help him with his Movements. "Rosaline?" exclaimed Romeo indignantly, "Not at all! She is a wet blanket, that's what she is! I did not even dance with her, because she told me she was tired. Tired at her age! She doesn't get the right kind of sleep, if you ask me! No, it wasn't Rosaline! Can you see that ravishing Mask with such divine vital statistics?" "What, that one with the grey hair and, I should say, vintage statistics?" "No, Mercutio, that is the Mother Mask!" "Woe and desolation!" exclaimed Mercutio, "the Mother Mask is Mrs Capulet!" Thus did Romeo learn the cruel truth that he was irremediably in love with Juliet, the heiress of Capulet Ltd, the bitter enemy of Montague Inc.

While the two friends were thus taken up with

statistical problems, there crept up on them Juliet's cousin, Tybalt, a most reactionary knave, the head of the ultra-feudalists and an expert phonetician who had recognized Romeo's voice by his defective pronunciation of certain sounds. Tybalt went up to Romeo and soundly slapped his face in the name of coexistence. Romeo was justly angered by such uncultured behaviour and would have replied in kind but for the intervention of Mr Capulet, who told them confidentially : "If you want to fight, lads, get outside! I don't want no scandals in my Palais!" Mr Capulet was a self-made commercial shark and had only a rough notion of grammar. But nevertheless, the slap resounded through the ballroom—which had wonderful acoustics—and so Juliet learned that she was helplessly in love with Romeo Montague, the implacable enemy of Capulet Ltd.

Finally, the band played the parting song "A Riverderci Verona", but Romeo was still lingering on the premises when he suddenly decided to jump over the fortified wall into the orchard of the Capulet Family, where Juliet, a keen scientist, used to experiment in crossing various species of plants. There, in the scented darkness, under an old plum-tree, Romeo sank into a sweet sentimental reverie. Suddenly, a candle glimmered at one of the windows, and Juliet stuck out her pretty head. In the silence of the night was heard the velvety voice of the Capulet heiress talking to herself in medieval parlance, a widespread habit in the fettered feudalistic era. "O, Romeo, wherefore art thou Romeo and belongest to Montague Incorporated? Oh, may the easing of tension thou spokest about take place very soon!" And Juliet, whilst she spoke, was leaning her cheek upon her hand and

Romeo passionately wished himself a glove upon that hand to touch her pretty face; then she put her hand upon her breast and sighed, whereupon Romeo became bolder in his reverie. Juliet, thinking she was alone, unburdened her heart of all the fire of her love for Romeo. Great was her amazement when Romeo himself joined in the conversation from under the plum-tree, unveiling in his turn the burning embers of his own heart. Juliet gently chid Romeo for jumping over the wall, instead of using a conventional crossing point, because he might have broken a leg or done himself some other bodily harm, or if the Capulet guards had caught him they would surely have crippled him for life. And then Juliet asked with true feminine cunning: "And what brought you here into the garden, Mr Montague—our delicious plums?" "Oh, Miss Capulet, oh, my Juliet, you are the forbidden fruit I am hankering for!" And Juliet hearing this, blushed profusely, but in the dark, it passed unnoticed. Romeo passionately pleaded with her to let him come up to her balcony for confidential high-level talks, without the glaring publicity of fashionable parties.

Juliet was sorry indeed that Romeo had heard her talking to herself: in the first place he might think her insane, and secondly she did not like the idea of confessing her love at the outset. She would have liked to grill him a little on the embers of love before saying "yes", as was the accepted procedure of the debutantes of the feudal era, in contrast with modern Socialist girls who get straight to the point. "Anyway, it's too late now!" she consoled herself and wanted to continue the loving conference with Romeo, who had already scaled the balcony with the help of a rope (he was a good social climber and had done the rope trick before) when into the dead of the night came the piercing voice of her old nurse, a woman of the people with strong Renaissance leanings. "Hey, Miss Juliet, don't dilly-dally on the balcony, dear: the temperature is 42 degrees Fahrenheit or 10 degrees centigrade (meteorology was her hobby) and you might catch a chill! Be a good Capulet girl and come inside!" "Let's adjourn the conference," Juliet whispered tenderly and gently pushed Romeo down the rope, pricking her cute ears until she heard a thump on the ground, heralding his safe landing. But as the old nurse had gone out of the room to do some hand-ablutions, Juliet popped out again on the balcony in a gossamer-like night-gown and Romeo, beholding this vision of delight, felt a potent urge to marry her at once. "Hey, you, under the plum-tree," whispered Juliet, "if you have honourable intentions I'll send a messenger tomorrow and fix the date of our wedding." And with this she concluded the meeting, blew out the candle and pulled the blinds. The cocks were crowing all over Verona. It was the break of day.

Romeo was so happy and restless that he could not sleep, so he went to Father Lorenzo, a progressive priest in the Renaissance Movement, to whom he confided all the details about his struggle for coexistence. The priest had just been reciting the Lord's Prayer when Romeo burst into his cell. "She certainly keeps you on tenterhooks, this Rosaline," commented Father Lorenzo bitterly, "to call on a priest at such ungodly hours!" "How can you say such things, Father?" retorted Romeo, "that girl is always tired, and secondly she doesn't care about coexistence! No, this time it's the real thing and her name is Juliet."

"What, not Juliet Capulet?" exclaimed the Father Confessor in horror, and when Romeo nodded in assent, the priest exploded: "You must be out of your mind! How can you imagine for one moment that Capulet Ltd will let you have her! Have you forgotten there is a cold war on?" "Alas! How could I forget?" replied Romeo sadly. "But I love Juliet and, what's more, she loves me. And please bear in mind, Father," added Romeo rather cunningly, "that if you marry us, tension will be eased and coexistence will become a reality!" Here he was touching a soft spot, because Father Lorenzo was a strong supporter of the policy of coexistence. After finishing the Lord's Prayer, Father Lorenzo said resolutely: "All right, count me in! Bring the bride tomorrow and I'll fix you up!"

Next day, with the nurse as best man, and after a brief ceremony during which Romeo and Juliet fainted in turn, such was their emotion, they were proclaimed man and wife and Romeo gave his bride, according to the custom in the feudal era, a wedding ring and a chastity belt. But great misfortune was in store for our star-crossed lovers.

The same day about noon, Mercutio was gaily strolling down the main boulevard of Verona, exchanging greetings with his friends and admirers, and just at the moment when he was making a deep bow to a young widow with Renaissance ideas, somebody kicked him from behind and caused him to lose his balance. He looked back in anger and there stood Tybalt, barring his way. Tybalt began to heap insults on everything he held dear, starting with the Renaissance and ending with the young widows whose friendship he cultivated for political reasons. By a

31

stroke of ill-fortune, Romeo passed the same way, happily whistling a Veronese wedding march, and still covered with the rice Father Lorenzo and the nurse had showered on him after the ceremony. Alas, as the turn of events is about to show, this was going to be "bitter rice". When Tybalt saw him coming, he stopped insulting Mercutio and turned on him, addressing him scathingly: "Hey, you, Montague puppy!" Romeo tried to reason with him, calling him cousin and explaining at the same time the advantages of the easing of tension. "I'll ease your tension all right!" threatened Tybalt rolling up his sleeves, and when he tried to ease him up, as he put it, Romeo withdrew strategically behind a pillar. Mad with fury, Tybalt jumped on Mercutio and stabbed him in the back. "This is more than a progressive-minded young man can stand!" shouted Romeo. "Who do you think you are, killing the Renaissance Organizer for the North of Italy?" Even as he was saying this long sentence, he drew his sword and slew Tybalt in honest combat.

In the meantime a big crowd had assembled on the boulevard, causing a huge traffic jam, with carriage drivers vociferating and swearing at the top of their voices. This bedlam roused the Prince of Verona, that UNO of feudalism, from his afternoon sleep. He left his headquarters at once to investigate a situation which, according to his mind, was a threat to peace; and when he arrived on the spot he saw two corpses and our friend Romeo with a blood-stained weapon in his hand. "I've caught you red-handed," exclaimed the Prince, "and I am going to show you now that my institution has teeth!" The representatives of the two rival trusts had also hurried to the spot, Mrs Capulet tearing out her hair, lamenting Tybalt's death and demanding sanctions against Romeo, and Mrs. Montague, also tearing out Mrs. Capulet's hair, defending her son and bemoaning Mercutio's murder. "Wait a moment, good citizens," said the Prince, "don't panic!" and after consulting the Charter of Verona, which he carried in his pocket, he applied sanctions to Romeo, proclaiming him "persona non grata" and ordering his deportation in forty-eight hours.

With a heavy heart, Romeo went to Father Lorenzo to ask his advice and, once there, he was seized by despair and began to rock and roll on the floor and knock his head against the walls with such force that the plaster started coming off in a big way. "Stop that!" commanded the priest, "You will ruin my cell! I'll think of something!" and he began reciting the Lord's Prayer as a prelude to meditation. After a while, his kindly face lit up and he said: "I got an idea! Go this evening to Juliet, consummate the marriage if you can, and at dawning, jump on a stage-coach to Mantua—there is one at 6.30—and there you will be met by friends from the Renaissance Movement. Stay with them and each day I'll send carrier-pigeons with news bulletins about events in Verona. When I think the time ripe, I'll issue a communique about your wedding and send invitations for a Summit Meeting, and, God willing, we might still ease the tension. What do you say, son?" Romeo stopped rolling on the floor and after packing a few night-shirts and other medieval clothes in a trunk, took position at dusk under the old plum-tree in Juliet's orchard, Juliet having been previously informed by a love-bird of what was coming. When darkness enveloped Verona, he climbed on the balcony where Juliet was blushingly waiting for him with two cups brimfull of love potion.

The first night of coexistence passed much too quickly and already the dawn was near and the early birds could be heard singing and catching worms. "Hark!" exclaimed Romeo, "Is it the nightingale or the lark?" evidently preferring the former bird. "It is definitely the lark," replied Juliet who was an expert bird-watcher and could identify them easily, "get dressed and be on your way!" But Romeo was loth to go and pleaded: "Give me five minutes more! Only five minutes more!" and he entreated her so nicely that Juliet had almost granted his request, when suddenly they heard the peremptory voice of the nurse who knocked on their door, after removing the "Don't disturb" sign appended there: "Hurry up, Master, or you'll miss the stage-coach!" And surely he would have missed it, but fortunately it arrived half an hour late, due to a go-slow strike of the drivers, profoundly dissatisfied with the poor pay they received from the feudalists. After an uneventful journey, Romeo arrived in Mantua, where he was duly met by a Renaissance representative who carried his trunk to a nearby inn.

Misfortunes do not come singly and Mr Capulet, unaware of his daughter's first marriage, decided to marry her again to Count Paris, the rich armament manufacturer, who had just pulled off a big deal by selling arms to a reactionary movement in France who were blowing up the residences of liberal-minded aristocrats. Juliet, being afraid of bigamy, invoked all sorts of pretexts to postpone the marriage, either that she was too young and wanted to have first a "taste of honey"—of dances and parties—or that she was still in mourning for cousin Tybalt; but Mr Capulet, who thought that this marriage would help him in a take-over bid for Montague Inc, was adamant.

Juliet, unable to cope with this tricky situation any longer, called on Father Lorenzo to ask for his advice, because the priest himself would have got into trouble if she was to be married again and he would have had his marrying licence revoked. "Holy mackerel!" the priest exclaimed devoutly when he was acquainted with the facts, "We are in thick soup indeed! Will you excuse me a moment, this calls for meditation!" and he quickly disappeared into an inner cell. When he came out of it, he said calmly: "There is nothing that a few pills can't fix!" holding in his hand a bottle with some medicine inside. "Go home and affect gaiety. Agree to the marriage, and the night before your second wedding take these sleeping pills, specially prepared by me, because, alas, I'm a sufferer from insomnia and the counting of sheep is no longer effective. Three will do the trick and you will sleep like a log for forty-two hours. Everybody will think that you are stone-cold dead and you will be taken by hearse to the family vault where Romeo, warned by a fast carrier-pigeon, will come and carry you stiff to Mantua where he will soften you up according to a magic formula, and then you will live happily ever after! How about that?" Juliet agreed reluctantly, firstly because she did not like taking medicine, and secondly she suspected that it might be poison so that the priest could get rid of her and keep his marriage bureau open. But the alluring vision of being carried away by Romeo—insensate as she might be—had a decisive influence.

When she returned home, she sang lustily in

French, as a means of deception, "Sous les toits de Paris", thus implying to her father that she would welcome a change of address, and old Mr Capulet, who had set his heart on the marriage to Count Paris, was overjoyed. Nevertheless, when she entered her bedroom, where she had heard the lark with Romeo, she broke down and wept. With a trembling hand, she took three pills out of the bottle, ground them to a powder—she could not swallow bitter pills—and drank them with a glass of water. The effect was instantaneous and she fell like a log on to the carpet. When the nurse came in the evening to help her with her curlers and saw her lying on the floor, she began to scream frantically: "Help, help, Miss Juliet has dropped dead!"

When Count Paris came next morning with an orchestra to wake her up, as was the wedding custom in Verona, he found his prospective bride frigid. The Capulets immediately altered the invitations, wrote "funeral" instead of "wedding" and dispatched them to the guests, with many outward signs of grief.

Father Lorenzo, considering on second thoughts that the news was too momentous to entrust to a carrier-pigeon, sent a young friar as a special emissary to Romeo, in Mantua, but this friar stopped in a monastery on his way there, and became so engrossed in a conversation about sects with the monks, that he completely forgot about his errand. And so Romeo read the sad news in the local paper, under the headline: "Capulet Heiress Dies", and he was desperate. He decided to kill himself, because life without Juliet was simply not worth living. As means of suicide he chose poison, unfortunately a commodity hard to get in Mantua where its sale was prohibited.

After walking the streets disconsolately for some time, he noticed a dilapidated chemist's shop with fly-blown notices in the window, such as : "Quick Remedies fot the Plague and Cholera. Love Potions. A Loving Cup Given Free with 3 Love Potions!" Romeo surmised rightly that the poor devil would sell anything to keep himself in business, so he entered the shop and said: "Good morning." "Good knight, how can I help you?" the chemist replied, rubbing his hands at the unexpected sight of a customer. Romeo briefly stated his business and the chemist demurred for a while; but when Romeo showed him a fat bundle of money he succumbed to temptation and said: "I've got the very stuff you want! A poison that would polish off twenty men like you, no disrespect intended!" and he handed him from under the counter, a phial simply labelled: "The Mixture. Take one dose in a lifetime."

But before taking poison Romeo wanted to have another look at his late wife, so he returned secretly to Verona. He headed straight for the Capulet vault and, once there, tried to open Juliet's tomb with a crow-bar. While he was thus employed, who should walk in but Count Paris, also intending to pay his last respects to his dead future wife. Seeing Romeo struggling and sweating in his frantic efforts to open the tomb, Paris suspected that he was there to desecrate the vault. Being under the influence of Capulet propaganda, Paris thought the Montagues capable of any crime in the book and construed Romeo's action as a revenge for the sanctions the Prince had applied to him. He pulled out his sword and assaulted Romeo. In the "duel macabre" that ensued in the vault, Paris was mortally wounded and his frightened retainer ran away screaming like mad. "That was quick work," said Romeo to himself and resumed his efforts which had been so unpleasantly disturbed. Eventually, he succeeded in removing the tomb-stone, took a last look at his seemingly dead wife, swallowed the Mixture and passed out.

The forty-two hours had elapsed by now, and Juliet, until then a sleeping beauty, opened her big eyes and, peering closely into the darkness of the vault, discerned her two husbands lying dead beside her bier. Thus, widowed twice over, she decided to end the life she had just regained. Guessing that Romeo had taken poison, she thought she would end her life in a similar way, so she kissed his stiff upper lip a couple of times; but without any visible results. In desperation, she wrenched a stiletto heel from one of her shoes and stabbed herself to death.

Father Lorenzo, looking at his hour-glass, noticed that the forty-two hours had gone by without any news from Romeo or the monk-emissary, and suspected that something had gone wrong. He hurried to the vault to let Juliet out of her tomb in case she was still there and disappointed that things had not gone according to plan and sadly weeping in her bier. When Father Lorenzo reached the cemetery he heard suspicious noises and commotion in the vault and, taken with fright, he ran away. After a wild chase around the tomb-stones in the graveyard, he was caught by the Veronese Police and taken to the vault, where the Capulets and the Montagues, alerted by the screaming retainer, had already assembled together with the Prince. They had been puzzled by so many fresh corpses, but when Father Lorenzo was brought in he explained it all, telling them about the secret marriage of Romeo and Juliet and how they had planned the easing of tension by their nuptials.

All the people present were shattered by these confessions and Messrs Capulet and Montague embraced each other and swore to sign a merger of their companies for the benefit of Verona; but one knows what little credence can be attributed to the "promises" of exploiters. Anyway, the Big Three Conference, so much desired by the young lovers, finally took place. The participants at the conference decided at the end of their otherwise inconclusive deliberations to erect a monument to the memory of the star-crossed lovers, with the epitaph:

"HERE LIE ROMEO AND JULIET,
VICTIMS OF THE COLD WAR".

King Lear

THE play "King Lear" by William Shakespeare, has a less pronounced political character than his other plays, being rather of a moral and philosophical nature.

The most important of the "dramatis personae" is King Lear II of Britain, a monarch who in his young days had had an advanced mentality and had tried to lighten the deep medieval darkness around him like a progressive-minded glow worm of history. With age, King Lear had abandoned the progressive ideas of his youth and turned into a staunch Conservative, with chauvinistic tendencies, pledging himself to make Britain "Great", and as such he is claimed as the founder of the British Tory Party, which is still governing the land with an iron-hand and pay-pauses.

It is interesting to note that King Lear's last direct descendant was Prince Edward, a writer, who under the simple name of Edward Lear was the author of a very amusing book.

The play shows us King Lear II in his ripe old age, in his middle 80's to be precise, and a bit tired by the cares of state. Although King Lear had moments when he felt quite strong and ebullient and used to say optimistically: "Life begins at eighty," such

40

moods were transient and on his 86th birthday he decided to retire from active life and write his "memoirs" so long overdue, eventually published under the title: "The Lay of an Ancient Briton".

Lear was the delayed father of three charming daughters by a second marriage and he fondly referred to them in French as "Les Girls". (His first wife had died barren at an old age and he had taken a much younger one in her bedstead.) "Les Girls" had brought him much joy and comfort in his vintage years and they had embellished his castle with frills and ribbons, and other such feminine touches, turning it into a real "Dolls' House". King Lear doted on them and when his memory failed him at times and he could not identify them properly, his darling daughters used to pull at his long white beard with much giggling and laughter.

His three girls were, in the order of their appearance on the stage of life: Goneril, now married to the Duke of Albany, a naturalized nobleman of Albanian extraction; Regan, married to the Duke of Cornwall, the owner of an English province much favoured by tourists where he was running an ancient holiday camp; and Cordelia, the youngest and the apple-strudel of Lear's eyes (German expression), because he had begotten her when he was very old and against all expectations. Cordelia had not yet tasted the bliss of matrimony and was jointly wooed by the King of France and the Duke of Burgundy, this latter a rich wine-grower with pink cheeks and a red nose. They had been staying as paying guests at Lear's court for the last six months to do their wooing, a very lengthy affair in those days, more like Five Year Plans.

King Lear's idea on retiring from active life was to institute a "troika" to rule his kingdom, in other words to entrust it to the delicate hands of his three daughters. But before drawing up the legal papers he wanted to check once more on their loyalty and affection, and so he arranged a "love contest" in the presence of his courtiers, who were to act as a panel of judges.

He questioned the girls in turn, according to their age, and, with pencil and paper in hand, was ready to take down their replies, while the courtiers had to determine by their applause which was the winning answer.

"Now, let's start!" said Lear, after a fanfare was sounded, "How much do you love me, Goneril?" he asked his eldest daughter. "I love you, Papa," came the suave reply, "more than my eyesight, my hearing or my smell, or any other of my senses, in fact I love you, Papa chéri, more than my own Albanian!"— the Duke of Albany, her husband. Lear was delighted and the courtiers' applause was loud and clear. "Thank you, Goneril!" said the King and handed her a document with one third of the kingdom, kissing her on both cheeks.

Then he addressed himself to the second contestant: "And now, how about you, Regan?" "I love you, Papa," she said fondling his beard with feigned affection, "even more than Goneril, and all the other joys of life leave me cold, including marriage, and, as I always say to my Cornish husband: 'My Heart Belongs to Daddy!'" "I made a hit with this one, too!" thought Lear with visible satisfaction, and the volume of the courtiers' applause was even stronger than before. "Thank you, Regan," said the King, handing her the second third of his realm with affectionate kisses, "bless you for being an angel!"

Now he turned to Cordelia, the apple-strudel of his eyes, from whom he expected the winning answer and had kept in reserve the biggest third of his domains. But Cordelia was thoroughly disgusted with the insincere flattery of her elder sisters who were nothing else but horrible career girls, in search of material gain. Because, as Cordelia reasoned: "If they are so fond of father, what the inferno are they doing in their husbands' beds?" So Cordelia said simply, in Basic English: "I love you, father, according to my duty; no more, no less!" and only scattered applause greeted her reply.

The old man was at first dumbfounded—he didn't expect such reticence—but then he got angry and ordered Cordelia to try again and express her love in more colourful language if she wanted to retain her third of the inheritance, adding bitterly: "I spent a lot on you at the best finishing schools in the country to learn English composition, so I have the right to demand a better declaration of love." Cordelia replied, at this final demand, with much dignity in her voice: "Thank you, father, for giving me life in your old age, against heavy odds, and, thanks also, for my education, because I know the large number of illiterate people in the Middle Ages, but to say more it would mean to flatter you, to create of you a personality cult, and this I simply cannot do!" King Lear, realizing that he could not extort a more elaborate love-confession, lost his temper and shouted: "Leave my palace, you ungrateful daughter, and get lost!" and he at once got his lawyers to disinherit her and remove her name from the "troika". Deeply shocked by her father's intemperate behaviour, Cordelia and her nurse-in-waiting "exeunt" with dignified steps.

Then Lear took a coronet from out of a box, and with a symbolic gesture he gave half a crown to Goneril and half a crown to Regan, proclaiming them joint winners of the contest. Finally, he signed the solemn contract, enabling the two deceitful daughters to avoid paying death duties and other heavy taxation upon his demise.

He kept for himself only the title of "Honorary King" and the right to have a retinue of 100 knights, to guard him from stray dogs and other wild beasts of the Middle Ages.

The right to a retinue was an old medieval privilege, and the retinue were supposed to follow their master everywhere: even when he went out, let's say, to wash his hands, the retinue followed him and waited patiently at the door, exactly in the same way as the Politburo had acted under Stalin.

Also in the contract it was stipulated that after his abdication, ex-King Lear should be kept for a full calendar month by each sister in turn (with all expenses paid) according to a rota yet to be fixed. The contract was then submitted to a referendum of the courtiers and it was approved with a handsome majority.

This document, guided by passion and not by reason, deeply grieved the progressive-minded courtiers who could already foresee its terrible consequences. Among those courtiers, the most advanced was the Earl of Kent, a man from the people on whom Lear had conferred a life peerage, who did not shrink from criticizing in the sharpest terms the wrong decision of the monarch. But Lear, not accepting criticism from below, got furious and ordered him to shut up if he valued his life peerage. But Kent refused to "shut up" and so King Lear banished him to live abroad, a cruel punishment totally unknown in Communist countries. Kent intended at first to emigrate to America, to start a new life there, but hearing that the immigration quota was full for the next two years, he decided to stay in Britain and continue the struggle as an outlaw. The candid criticism of the Earl of Kent had only aggravated the King's wrath and made him behave like a frantic patient who wants to kill his physicians, very similarly to another old tyrant, I. V. Stalin, who shortly before his death had invented the "doctors' plot".

When hearing of Cordelia's loss of face and dowry, her wooers acted differently: the Duke of Burgundy —the greedy wine-merchant—gave up his suit and "exit", while the King of France was ready, as he put it, to take Cordelia even with nothing on her back— and front—because in Fair France they had wonderful couturiers who were sure to make her a splendid trousseau. Then he gave Cordelia, as pre-marital gifts, a large bottle of French perfume called "Chanel 5"—sounding nowadays like a television programme—and a smaller one, called "Middle Age Desire", specially to be used at the social functions for the French elder statesmen. The King of France also upbraided the Duke of Burgundy, before his "exit", for his unchivalrous behaviour and warned him solemnly: "From now on, Burgundy, keep your nose out of Cordelia's affairs!"

Cordelia, with wet eyes, took leave of her sisters and implored them to take good care of their father, but these termagants told her to mind her own

45

business and strive to content her sentimental French husband, who has taken her with no clothes on her back.

Even before the expiry of the first month, which according to the rota, ex-King Lear was spending with his eldest daughter, Goneril, he noticed the big gap between pledges and achievements. Although he had given Goneril, in an outburst of magnanimity, even the crown from his head—so that he now went bareheaded in all weathers—the Duchess frowned on him when she met him in the corridors followed closely by his 100 knights, to whom she contemptuously referred as "The Crazy Gang"; and at meals she counted every mouthful of food eaten by Lear and his retinue. His expense sheet was never met and her servants refused to obey his orders, or else pretended not to hear him like dumb waiters in a second-class restaurant. They treated him with scorn imitating their wicked mistress; they left his bed unmade and his shoes unpolished and even forgot to bring him at breakfast his favourite paper: "The Ancient Britain Chronicle". Poor Lear, what could he do, his property had been, so to say, nationalized, he was nothing but an ex-King! Lear noticed the alteration in his daughter's behaviour but he shut his eyes against it, unwilling to believe the unpleasant consequences of his own folly.

The Earl of Kent, as we know, did not go abroad and, disguised as a servant, he managed, through an employment agency, to be hired by the ex-King as his personal attendant, to help him dress in the morning and to tuck him in bed at night. To keep his identity secret, Kent took now the alias of Caius, and Lear, whose eyesight had been rather poor of late, did not notice the trick. One day, the chief lackey of Goneril was very impudent with the ex-King, and Caius got so furious that he kicked him behind the belt, and Lear was delighted and raised his salary.

Another positive "dramatis persona" is the Fool, in fact a wise man, who although no longer paid after the abdication, had faithfully followed his master into retirement. The Fool, or Jester, a VIP in the Middle Ages, was the only one who could criticize the King freely, playing the part of the "Opposition" in bourgeois parliaments, while in the Soviet Union, of course, the Fool is kept in his proper place, which is the circus. Lear's Fool often satirized his master and made him a figure of fun, saying that he had spent his money on girls and had now become a "proper pauper with a weirdy beardie".

After a fortnight, the Duchess Goneril came with angry mien to ex-King Lear and stormed into his bedroom, without knocking on the door, thus finding him in an embarrassing position, still in his night-shirt while Caius was singeing his beard with a torch. Goneril ordered her father to cut his retinue by half and keep only the old knights, of his own age, because they were more at peace in certain respects and did not chase the chamber-maids as the younger ones were wont to do. The ex-King was deeply offended by such aspersions on his retinue, and also for breaking into his bedroom like this, and called her a monster and a liar, without proper house-training. He ordered his horses to be saddled at once because he did not want to stay a moment longer under the roof of an ungrateful daughter. "I am going ahead of the rota to Regan," shouted Lear, "you'll see how nicely she takes care of me!"

47

Before his departure, he cursed Goneril not to bear any children, not even by artificial insemination, and if she managed to get around his curse with the help of her husband, to bear in that case only ungrateful children. The Fool also poked fun at Goneril, wishing her to become an "Uncanny Mammy with Besmirching Urchins", for which he was promptly whipped by the enraged Duchess in no mood to tolerate the pranks of the "Opposition". The loud shrieks of the whipped Fool—now bitterly regretting his keen sense of humour—brought the Duke of Albany from his study where he was just reading a long letter from Albania, and he apologized to Lear, in broken English, for any inconvenience caused by his wife, entreating him to grace them with his presence a little longer. Moved by the solicitude of his alien son-in-law, Lear agreed to postpone his departure for a couple of days, but he was, nevertheless, determined to go.

Leaving ahead of the rota, he sent Caius before him, as his personal messenger, to tell Regan to prepare 103 rooms, that is, for him, his retinue, and his two personal attendants. Goneril, on the other hand, had despatched to Regan, as her own messenger, the notorious chief lackey who, as we know, had been kicked behind the belt by Caius, and when the two messengers met on the way, Caius repeated the treatment, even more vigorously than before, with the result that the chief lackey could not sit properly in the saddle and had to walk the last few miles. When Regan heard of the treatment, she put Caius in stocks and bonds as a punishment, although he was a royal messenger and as such entitled to diplomatic immunity.

When Lear arrived and saw Caius in the stocks said: "I do not like the sight of this!" and he hurried to extricate his faithful servant from this disgraceful position and raised his salary again to comfort him. An even more disagreeable surprise was in store for Lear when Regan and her Duke informed him through a second-class nurse that they could not see him, because they were rather "tired". Old Lear got really worked up and shouted: "You'll see me right away!" and went straight to their bedroom and banged violently on the door. After some hasty confabulation behind closed doors, the doors opened wide and: "lo and behold!" Together with the couple stepped out the viper Goneril, who had taken a short cut and arrived at the castle before him. "How dare you, female monster, show your face again and look upon my white beard?" Lear had barely time to say, because what followed surpassed any trick of imagination and left him speechless. Regan said: "Don't get excited, father, it isn't good at your age! Better ask to be forgiven by my dear sister and return to her according to the rota. And by the way, I also think that you should reduce your military budget and cut down on your 'Crazy Gang'; in any case most of your knights are redundant and they do nothing but run after chamber-maids!" "This is a monstruous lie!" protested Lear indignantly, "My knights are perfect gentlemen and self-contained! Why should they run after ignorant chamber-maids when they have the Fool to keep them amused? Good Heavens, if I am treated in this way by my own daughters, I will go to strangers, to my French son-in-law, who will certainly give me a pension, and I heard that in France, beside their monthly allowance,

49

old-age pensioners are getting a barrel of wine extra."
Regan pretended not to hear, and continued: "I
consider that even twenty-five knights are too many!"
Lear did some rapid arithmetic in his head and
replied: "In that case I prefer to return to Goneril;
at least she guarantees me fifty knights!" But Goneril
went back on her word: "But why do you need
twenty-five, or even ten or five? I think you should
fire them all! My servants will take care of you!"
And suddenly through Lear's mind flashed the image
of unmade beds and unpolished shoes, and he laughed
bitterly. He felt he was losing his senses. His daughters were making fun of him, they wanted complete
disarmament! "If such is your filial devotion, I will
go out in the fields with my loyal knights, we shall
sleep in the open, the birds of Heaven will feed us
with worms!" and he leaned out of the window and
ordered: "Retinue! Mount your horses!" but the
retinue had simply vanished, because having heard of
the painful disarmament talks going on in the castle
and guessing rightly that from now on they would
lead the rough life of knights errant, with no proper
mess arrangements or fixed abode, they had "exeunt"
on the quiet without giving Lear the customary one
week's notice.

So Lear had to go out in the fields alone, with Caius
and the Fool. It was a terrible night and it was rain-
ing. Of course that in itself was not serious—just the
usual British weather—but there was also thunder and
lightning, and a gale warning had just been issued.
The Fool was pouring out his jokes, on and on: "Well,
Lear if you have spent your money on girls, it serves
you right!" until the old man, in a fit of anger, slapped
his face and the Fool shut up. Caius noticing that the

water was streaming down his master's locks and beard, making him look like "Ol' Man River"—a pagan deity—and furthermore, hearing him sneeze, thought with anguish: "Goodness Gracious me! The Sovereign will catch cold and it is no joke at his age!" But Lear ignored his watery condition, being taken up with destructive thoughts: he was solemnly bidding the gales blow the earth into the sea or the waves drown the earth and if by any miracle he could have got hold of an H-Bomb he would surely have dropped it right away on Ancient Britain. Hearing his master's voice ranting like this, Caius was terribly alarmed and after much pleading convinced the ex-King to enter a little hut by the roadside.

There, they were surprised to see a crazy old beggar in a wretched plight, with nothing but a wet blanket over his loins, to cover his nakedness. Lear imagined, in his disturbed mind, that he was a nudist father who had given all away to his daughters and started to tell the poor beggar that they were both fellow-fathers with problem children, making Caius realize that he was actually going mad. With soothing words and cradle songs, Caius tried to make his master rest for a while on a straw bed, but old Lear fretted and twisted the night away. Next morning, he interned Lear in a Mental Home for Customs Officers, near Dover, and he crossed into France to acquaint his daughter Cordelia with the cruel truth.

When the poor girl heard the facts, she started to weep and with tears in her eyes she went to her husband, the King of France, who was just having breakfast with his new mistress (Frenchmen have a simple life with only coffee and croissants for breakfast) and asked him to give her some French foreign legions to cross the Channel and restore her mad father to the throne.

In the meantime, Lear had escaped from the Mental Home and was roaming the countryside, wearing a star-spangled bath-robe and a Home-made crown, and this choice of clothes considerably facilitated the task of his recapture.

The physicians treated him by the new method of shock therapy, that is by telling him that Cordelia, or the King of France, or another person dear to him was dead, and then immediately denying the fact. In this way, Lear was temporarily cured and the delayed meeting with his daughter could be arranged. The reunion between repentant father and ever-loving daughter was so moving, and occasioned so much crying from both sides, that even the Fool broke down and wept for hours.

And now we come to the last part of the play, when the writer Shakespeare usually massacres all his characters. The two bad sisters got bored after a time with the same husbands and began to look for extra-connubial bliss. It so happened that both of them fell in love with the same gigolo, a scoundrel named Edmund, the illegitimate child of the Earl of Gloucester, a gentleman-farmer who, as a young man, had been rather careless sowing his wild oats. Having the good luck to lose her husband after the first dose of poison she had administered to him, Regan was as merry as a lark and proclaimed her intention of marrying Edmund at once. Devoured by jealousy, Goneril prepared a large tumbler with poison for her sister which she placed herself into her hand with the words: "Come on, drink to your future marriage, bottoms up!" Regan was so carried away by the idea of marriage that she drank it in one gulp and was dead. The Duke of Albany, hearing of the heinous crime of his wife, threw her in jail where she hanged herself with a blue stocking. Not even poor Cordelia was spared by Shakespeare, because Edmund, the lady-killer of the wicked sisters, routed the French foreign legions and captured Cordelia. On her resisting his advances, he imprisoned her in the famous Holloway prison and there the poor girl died of malnutrition and exposure (once more she had no clothes on her back). Hearing this, old Lear died too, and in his last days his reason was clouded again, so that he could not understand that Kent and Caius was one and the same person. Grieved by the fact that he was not properly identified, Kent, alias Caius, died also. The Fool, seeing so many mishaps around him, was deeply impressed and became a serious man for the rest of his life. The gigolo Edmund was killed in battle by the Duke of Albany, who ascended the throne and became the only British King of Albanian extraction.

From the play "King Lear" the Soviet people can learn a few useful lessons: that criticism from below is very important, because if Lear had taken into account the constructive criticism of Kent, he could have spared himself much suffering; that the cult of personality must be thoroughly discouraged, because if Lear had not listened to flattery and empty words he could have been a better judge of girls; and finally, that old men, on retiring from active work must have adequate pensions to ensure them a peaceful old age. We are proud to proclaim that in the Soviet state, where the aged and the invalids enjoy all requisite amenities, one can truly say, like King Lear, that:

LIFE BEGINS AT EIGHTY!

Hamlet

THE hero of the play is the Crown Prince Hamlet, a
young man from Denmark with advanced ideas but
sometimes given to complacency and day-dreaming.
He was the son of King Hamlet I, a progressive and
kind-hearted monarch, similar in many ways to Ivan
the Terrible, the Russian Czar. In the last years of his
reign, Hamlet I was seriously thinking of introducing
a vast land reform and in his table-talk he often referred to the "winds of change", without, however,
elaborating on the subject. His progressive-minded-
ness won him the love of the common people, who
called him "The Great Dane", but, at the same time,
he incurred the implacable hostility of the aristocracy.
The aristocrats hatched many plots to overthrow him
until, one day, an official communique briefly stated
that King Hamlet I had died from the bite of a
poisonous snake. The communique was much dis-
believed at the time by the peasants, the more so when
they heard that the Danish Yard, the Copenhagen
Police, were prevented from investigating the remains
of the snake. The nobility illegally proclaimed
as their new king the brother of the deceased,
Claudius, whom Queen Gertrude, the widow of
"The Great Dane", has hastily married, with complete
disregard for the rules of mourning. The new King

Claudius was a pompous reactionary and a staunch upholder of feudalistic privileges, as can be deduced from his own memoirs, published during his reign under the title "I, Claudius".

The mysterious death of his father and the lascivious deportment of his mother—to whom courtiers alluded as "The Merry Widow"—had a deep impact on the mind of the young Prince Hamlet who became afflicted with that particular type of Nordic melancholy known as "Danish Blues". His scientific mind, when working, could not accept the official explanation, and he suspected foul play. He embarked on a thorough study of poisonous snakes and their habits, and the more he knew about them the more suspicious he grew.

One day he heard that a certain ghost, closely resembling his dead father, was making scheduled appearances on the walls of the Elsinore Palace, the Royal Castle. Ghosts, by the way, are a common sight in the Scandinavian countries and quite recently, a Norwegian author, named Ibsen, had written a successful play about them.

After much hesitation, Hamlet finally decided to scale the palace walls to meet this regular apparition. The ghost was supposed to come round about midnight, given a clear moon. Accompanied by his good friend Horatio and a sentry, he climbed up on the ramparts a short time before Zero Hour and began the count-down. He had to hold it twice, because there were some clouds around the moon and so the ghost could not come. Finally, when all was clear, he saw some bedlinen in the distance. It was the Ghost! When the ghost noticed that Hamlet was accompanied, he would not talk, but beckoned to the Prince with one of his bones to follow him for an exclusive interview. The good Horatio wanted to prevent him going alone, for fear that the ghost, in one of his facetious moods, might push him off the walls, but Hamlet replied firmly: "No matter what happens, I'll follow the poltergeist!"

As soon as they were alone, the ghost showed him all his bones, saying: "I am your father, but I've lost weight. I want you to know, son, that I was murdered!" And then he told him in detail how things had really happened: how on a Summer day, after luncheon, he had pushed his throne in the shade of a tree to have a nap, and how while he was asleep Uncle Claudius had come with a hose and poured poison in one of his ears, and how with only one good ear left he could not live and died shortly afterwards. And the fatherly ghost opened his jaw-bones, perhaps to tell him about the land reform, but the cock crowed and the ghost had to take off.

Hamlet Junior swore to avenge this horrible crime, and being completely satisfied now about the circumstances of the murder, interrupted his studies of poisonous snakes and ventured into the wider field of medicine.

We shall see now how these medical studies were to transform his personal "vendetta" into something more important, into a struggle with a pronounced social character. His medical preoccupations took him often to the local cemetery, the only place where he could find the skeletons necessary for his observations. There, in the cemetery, he met an exponent of the new way of life, a progressive-minded grave-digger of Russian extraction. He was no ordinary man, this grave-digger, but a real social revolutionary, and at night he used to meet like-minded persons in the crypts of the cemetery, they being, as it were, the first crypto-communists.

The grave-digger discussed with Hamlet various political matters and explained to him that something was rotten in the State of Denmark, namely the feudal system, and that only in a progressive state could medicine flourish.

After such an inspiring discussion, Hamlet spoke his famous soliloquy, starting with the words:

"To be or not to be with the people"

which was subsequently truncated by the feudalists and their bourgeois cousins.

Lines like that make the Soviet People love Shakespeare and the capitalists execrate him. Quite recently, an American magazine had the impudence to publish the following "cogitation" of a young Fascist: "Shakespeare was a square, even more so than Charles Dickens who at least had composed 'The Oliver Twist'."

Hamlet proceeded with enthusiasm to the preparation of the "coup détat" and in order to lull the vigilence of the Security organs, he simulated a "sweet madness", a half-way house between absent-mindedness and the mental home.

Hamlet, like every young man of his age, was consumed by the fire of love and he worshipped Ophelia, a distinguished botanist and the daughter of the Danish Prime Minister, Dr Polonius, a close friend of the usurper King. The two young people nurtured a healthy love, based on scientific leanings, and they used to meet often on the bank of the river, Hamlet showing his "bones" and Ophelia, her herbarium.

When Hamlet became busy with his "coup", directing the underground operations from his HQ in the
cemetery, he saw less of Ophelia and was devoured
by passion. In one of his spare moments he wrote her
a burning love letter, couched in the grandiloquent
style of the feudal era, when love was declared with
one knee on the floor and one hand on the heart, in
contrast to the Socialist love of today, declared in the
shade of the tractor.

Hamlet's love letter was duly shown by Ophelia to
her father, Dr Polonius, who asked at once to be
received in audience by the King and Queen. "Sire
and Siren," said Dr Polonius, "look what I've laid my
hands on! This explains the royal madness of Prince
Hamlet: he is crazy about my daughter!"

Incidentally, Prime Minister Polonius was a very
clever politician indeed, and despite the economic
misery of the population, he had managed to convince
the Danes that "they'd never had it so good".

In the meantime, Prince Hamlet had relapsed into
complacency and invoked a thousand pretexts to
postpone the "coup d'état"—either that the King was
too well guarded, or that the ideological indoctrina-
tion of his followers was not yet complete, or that
he was not sure that the ghost was really his father
and so forth, to the despair of the grave-digger who
did his best to egg him on.

In these moments of complacency, when Hamlet
just idled about and ate Danish Pastry, there arrived
a touring Danish Repertory Company of Merited
Actors. He went to their rehearsals of a play about
Priam and Hecuba, and was so deeply impressed by
the immaculate conception Hecuba had of a wife's
duties that he broke down and wept profusely. When

he recovered from this shattering experience he realized the propaganda value of the theatre and so, in order to unmask his uncle, he decided to stage with these actors a play strikingly similar to the poisoning of King Hamlet I.

The play was about a crime perpetrated in Vienna, in the former American sector, in which Duke Gonzago is killed by Lucianus, a close relation. Afterwards, Lucianus marries the wife of the deceased, Duchess Baptista. The murder takes place also in the garden and also under a tree.

Hamlet sent complimentary tickets to the King and Queen, thus making sure that they would come to see the play. The Queen got completely flustered when Duchess Baptista declared in a conversation with her husband Gonzago, shortly before the murder: "May I drop dead if I marry anyone after you!" But the faithless noblewoman married, posthumously, none other than the murderer. King Claudius, on the other hand, was glued to his seat when Lucianus entered the garden with a hose to poison Gonzago. Unable to stand the play any longer, Claudius left the theatre.

The Queen afterwards summoned Hamlet to her apartments to chide him for his queer behaviour of late. The King, very curious by nature, ordered Prime Minister Polonius to hide behind a curtain, to eavesdrop on the conversation.

The Queen said to Hamlet: "You offended your father with your conduct." "Uncle Claudius is not my father," replied Hamlet angrily, "and I know that you, Mamma, and Uncle Claudius poisoned my true father!" "Mind what you say," retorted the Queen, "because it will be held as evidence against you!" and was about to leave the room, but Hamlet caught her by the wrist and shook her. Believing that Hamlet was having one of his fits, the Queen began to scream. "Help, help, he's killing the Queen!" shouted Dr Polonius from behind the curtain considering himself invisible. Hamlet, suspecting that it was his uncle behind the curtain, began to stab it with his sword, and this not being an iron curtain, Dr Polonius was killed. Seeing the damage, the Queen said: "You, wretch, you'll rot in jail!" "Stop nagging, Mamma, I've only killed a Prime Minister!" replied Hamlet, now really furious. And he started to scold her something awful. He took from his pocket two portraits, one, artistic, of his own father, done by an Englishman named Beaton, and another one, like a passport picture, of Uncle Claudius. "Look at them, Mamma, and see your mistake! Look how handsome father was and how ugly Uncle Claudius is!" As he said this, he was waving the passport portrait of his uncle in her face. And while he was in the midst of his peroration, who should walk in but the ghost himself who, having sent his shroud to the laundry, was invisible to the Queen and only seen by Hamlet, now accustomed to ghosts. Noticing that Hamlet was talking to himself, or so at least she thought, the Queen was thoroughly convinced that her son was out of his mind.

Hearing of Polonius' assassination, the King wanted at first to sentence Hamlet to death but on second thoughts decided to send him to England, a Danish protectorate where it rained all the time. He gave Hamlet a letter of introduction to the ruling circles of England, ordering them to kill Hamlet as soon as he appeared at the customs. Hamlet, being a bright young man, thought to open the letter and read what was inside. So, with the flame of a candle, he gently opened the letter, read what was inside, and did not like it at all. He took a rubber, erased his name from the letter, put in its stead the names of the two courtiers accompanying him, Rosencrantz and Guildenstern, two naturalized Danes, and stuck back the envelope. After that he left for England.

Basking on the deck of his ship, Hamlet noticed in the distance a strange looking galleon flying a black flag with a skull and two bones. He imagined at first that she might carry a cargo of skeletons for medical studies but the sailors explained to him that they were pirates, sea-thieves. Hamlet, having known only land-thieves, was very curious indeed and he jumped into the galleon to fight the pirates. While he was so engaged, his own ship, with the two courtiers, left him to Marx's mercy and continued the voyage to England where the courtiers, according to the letter of introduction, were promptly killed. And serve them right!

As it is known, Soviet historians have already established that the pirates were not sea-thieves, but progressive-minded individuals who not yet having achieved power in the state—there were still many years to elapse before the October Revolution—were practising reforms from man to man.

As one would expect, the pirates—honest thieves—behaved nicely to Hamlet and put him ashore at the first Danish port they struck. From there, Hamlet sent a registered courier to the King, announcing he would come to Elsinore by the first stage-coach.

Hamlet's arrival coincided with a very sad event. Ophelia had died and was being taken by hearse to the Mausoleum. The poor girl-botanist had not been able to go on breathing the stifling atmosphere of feudalism, and had lost her mind. Seized with a deep melancholy—the Danish Blues—she divided her herbarium amongst her friends and with the few flowers remaining she had fashioned herself some personal adornments. Wearing around her neck garlands of daisies and nettles, Ophelia betook herself to the bank of the river where she'd had so many dates with Hamlet, and having made a "faux pas" she fell into the water. Being unable to swim—feudalistic girls were not allowed to practise any sports except marriage—she was caught up by the current and drowned. Hamlet, being a boy, could swim, but he had arrived too late.

The funeral procession passed in front of Hamlet who was hidden in the crowd. Immediately behind the hearse, Danish girl-botanists were marching ten abreast, and the five girls in each line were holding hands. It was a moving scene and Hamlet decided to follow them.

Ophelia's brother, Laertes, seeing Hamlet at the Mausoleum, fell on him and beat him up, and the two young men were separated only with great difficulty by the sad mourners. Hamlet apologized afterwards for being beaten, but the hatred between the two young men continued to smoulder.

King Claudius made use of these strained relations and urged Laertes to challenge Hamlet to a friendly duel, giving him the necessary velvet glove to slap Hamlet's face. (Velvet gloves were used for friendly duels.) Laertes, also at the King's prompting, and acting in complete disregard of sporting rules, put some poison on the tip of his foil.

The referee blew his whistle and the game began
in the big hall of Elsinor Palace. In the first few
rounds Hamlet led on points and was enthusiastically
cheered by the spectators and by the King himself
who, out of pure deceit, was drinking innumerable
cups of wine on the sidelines in honour of his nephew.
Laertes recovered the initiative and after some successful passes managed to scratch Hamlet's back with
the poisoned foil. In a scrum, the opponents changed
weapons by mistake and Hamlet was now in posses-
sion of the poisoned foil with which, in his turn, he
scratched Laertes.

While the game was thus proceeding and the wagers
were mounting—the bookmakers were doing brisk
business—the Queen in the Royal Box started to
scream that she had been poisoned, which was perfectly true, because she had drunk by mistake out of
a large cup of rat-poison, thoughtfully prepared by
Claudius in case Hamlet came unscratched from the
duel. On the cup with poison was written in big letters
"Coca-Cola", a brilliant idea of the Soviet producers
to satirize the Americans.

Hamlet stopped the play and shouted: "Shut the
doors; no one leaves this hall. It's a raid! We must
catch the murderer!" Laertes made a full confession
and showed the King as the murderer. "You hear that,
Uncle!" said Hamlet and plunged the poisoned foil
into his uncle's heart. But the poison in the Prince
also started to work and Hamlet, from his death-floor
—because they did not have the time to put him in
bed—requested his friend Horatio to inform progressive world opinion of the misdeeds perpetrated at the
Danish Court.

You can rest assured, Sweet Prince, that world

opinion is now fully cognizant of all the misdeeds of the oppressors, and the intellectuals of the Soviet Union have already answered the question, which should be asked by honest intellectuals everywhere:

"TO BE OR NOT TO BE WITH THE PEOPLE!"

Othello

Colonialist literary critics have held for centuries
that the moral of the play "Othello" is the avoidance
of mixed marriages, in other words that White is White
and Black is Black and never the twain should meet,
because if they do, they invite the most dire consequences, including murder by strangulation. But on
the contrary, William Shakespeare teaches us that the
marriage of Othello and Desdemona would have been
blissfully consummated if decadent feudalist society,
the sworn enemy of the progressive Renaissance ideas,
had not interfered in their internal affairs.

This Shakespearian play is set in Venice, a pictur-
esque town in Italy, where the Municipal Council,
bent on enriching themselves, had shown criminal in-
difference to the welfare of the people by allowing
the streets to lie full of water, so that the citizens
should incur rheumatism and thus be unable to revolt.

At the time of our play, there lived in Venice the
famous General Othello, a coloured officer serving in
the Venetian Army as honourable Black Mercenary.
He had been born in Ghana, in the progressive con-
tinent of Africa, and his real name was Ngotello

which he had to change because the uncultured Venetian feudalists could not pronounce it properly.

As soon as he reached the Italian shores he secretly joined the Renaissance Movement, a leftish movement which aimed at bringing social justice to Venice and other Italian cities and waged an unrelenting struggle against the "Reincarnation", a right-wing feudalist party. After a short time Othello became a member of the Central Committee of the Renaissance Front, which was, as its name implies, a front organization with the slogan: "For A Lasting Peace, For the Overthrow of Feudalism". It is not difficult to see why Othello made a secret of his membership because otherwise it would have jeopardized his job and his chances of enjoying a retirement pension.

The Renaissance Front was a wonderful organization for its period and among its many pursuits was the mobilization of the opinion of the man-in-the-canal (corresponding to the man-in-the-street in dry cities) against the use of gun-powder, then a most destructive weapon of war. The Renaissance Front organized protest meetings and its members were instructed to stage voluntary sit-down strikes, naturally not in the streets, which would have been damping for their enthusiasm, but in the main squares of the city. It is interesting to note that this Venetian way of protesting is still practised today in London and throughout the British Isles. From top to bottom—in other words from the Central Committee to the sit-down strikers—the Renaissance Front was a progressive movement, the forerunner of the Communist Party.

Venice was ruled by a decadent oligarchy headed by the Doge—the object of a nauseating personality

cult—and the Venetian Congress, a handful of reactionary senators, big shipowners and importers of
spices from the East. Among these feudalistic sharks
the most hated was undoubtedly Senator Brabantio,
the Chairman of the notorious Committee for the
Investigation of un-Venetian Activities. Needless to
say, the main targets of this witch-hunt were the
members of the Renaissance Movement, and many of
these true patriots were cast in jail by this Venetian
monster. Venice, once a happy city, was now known
as "The Blue Lagoon", on account of its pervading
sadness. The common people, with their rheumatism,
could not do much. They just shook their heads in
sorrow and sighed, hence the name of the famous
bridge.

But life is very strange to be sure, and the same
Senator Brabantio had a daughter, pure and beautiful, wise and modest, called Desdemona. The fair
Desdemona, although brought up in feudalistic
circles, was fortunate as a child to have a progressive
wet-nurse from the Renaissance Movement who had
instilled in her the milk of human kindness, love for
the common people.

Desdemona deeply resented the racial laws of
Venice and, as a protest, she frequently went, accompanied by her wet-nurse (who had run dry by now)
to "The Colour Bar", a pub near the Piazza San Marx
where coloured people used to meet. It must have
been very similar to Moscow's night-club "The Blue
Engels".

There, some enchanted evening, she saw General
Othello in the company of other coloured mercenaries
from the Venetian "Black Watch" Regiment, and was
fascinated by him. She at once took his roving eye—

she was wearing an evening gown with a deep décolleté, or as they say in Venice, a double-breasted suit—
and, as she confessed later, there and then she was
struck by Cupid's arrow.

And so, between Othello and Desdemona there was
born a sincere and passionate love based on their
mutual inclination for progress. After that, Othello
met Desdemona in secret many times, and once, when
they were travelling in a Number 11 Gondola (in
Venice they had gondola-lines) Othello disclosed that
he was a secret member of the Renaissance Front and
that he was fighting for freedom and the overthrow
of feudalism. Having complete confidence in her,
Othello told the young maiden about a top-secret plan
of his organization, the plan to blow up "The Powder
Room", the building where the Venetian authorities
kept their criminal stores of gun-powder.

The love became even more ardent when Othello
told Desdemona of his travels around the world on his
campaign for the abolition of gun-powder. He told
her how once he had entered the Black Sea, hoping
to see some fellow-Africans on its shores, but had the
unexpected privilege of meeting his first Russians, the
most advanced people in the Middle Ages, in which
condition they are still today. The Russians had a
burning love for peace—"Some Like It Hot" they
used to say about peace—which, naturally enough,
did not prevent them from testing their own peaceful
gun-powder in remote regions. At first, seeing that
Othello was black—a very uncommon sight in those
parts—the Russians were on the point of running
away from him, but when the General produced a
Venetian peace-dove out of his helmet, they became
very friendly indeed. General Othello told Desdemona

that when he retired from the Army he intended to write a series of articles about the Russians in a Venetian Sunday paper because he had met them for a couple of hours and was thus an expert on the subject.

Desdemona was so captivated by such tales and by the General's idea of progressive love that she proposed to him at once. Othello tried, rather half-heartedly, to dissuade her by pointing out the discrepancy in age and (alas!) in colour between them, but to no avail. The mixed lovers decided to get married at once, even without the consent of her parents. Not knowing that they could be married easily in Scotland, a country where parents are impotent, they were joined in secret matrimony by a progressive priest of the Renaissance Movement.

Senator Brabantio, noticing that they were now living together, became suspicious, and after being interrogated the lovers confessed that they were actually man and wife. One can well imagine the fury of Brabantio, who had wanted a White Wedding for his daughter. . . . He immediately sued Othello for violation of the racial laws of Venice, throwing in for good measure the charge of un-Venetian activities.

What hypocrisy! General Othello, the defender of Venice, to be called un-Venetian, when everybody knew the generosity he had shown towards his adopted city, how he had with his first salary built a magnificent hospital for the citizens of Venice who had lost their eye-sight, called "The Venetian Blinds". This preoccupation with the welfare of the common people was clearly a characteristic trait of the Renaissance Movement, because the members of the French Branch had built a hospital for mad shepherds called

"The Folies Bergeres". But a lot the rich senators cared for the common people and their ailments! And so brave Othello was to be tried, as was customary in such cases, by the Venetian Congress presided over by the Doge.

Now a few words about the actual proceedings of the trial. Senator Brabantio, an obscurantist shark, asserted that it was impossible for him to explain in rational terms the affection of a white maiden for a coloured gentleman, and so he was compelled to conclude that Othello had used black magic to seduce his daughter, a crime punishable by death in that age of superstition. If such mixed marriages were allowed, said Brabantio, the whole colour scheme of Venice would alter and before long their proud city might have a black Doge at its head. Deafening applause greeted the end of Senator Brabantio's speech and was warmly congratulated by his fellow-sharks.

Then General Othello rose and spoke for several hours in his own defence. The two themes of his defence were: 1. "Love Is A Many-Splendoured Thing" and 2. "Love Is Colour-Blind". He harangued them with such passion and conviction that when he finally sat down saying: "If there is no place for us in Venice, I'll take Desdemona home and make her an African Queen", all the senators were shedding secret tears because no matter how abject they might have been, all humans have the instinct for love, everybody is, as the Romans said, a Homo Sexualis! The Doge himself, visibly shaken and weeping profusely, acquitted Othello of all the charges and appointed him Governor of Cyprus, a very risky assignment.

Cyprus, a rugged island, ruled traditionally by turbulent clergymen, was a hotbed of intrigues and

70

plots, and many a time the Venetian Governor had found poisonous snakes in his bed, ready to take a bite at him. And on top of these considerable dangers, the Turkish pirates were making a real nuisance of themselves. Undaunted by the perils, Othello, at the head of a Peace Force set sail for the island accompanied by his bride and her progressive wet-nurse (extra-dry by now!).

When Governor Othello arrived in the island he was greeted with an enthusiasm surpassed only by the welcome extended to the Great Lenin when he returned to Petrograd in his German-sealed railway carriage in 1917. The Cyprus Folk Dance Ensemble were on the quay to greet him with some nimble footwork and the Greek Chorus girls kissed him on both cheeks.

Great was Othello's joy to meet, at landing, the Deputy Commander of the Cyprus Military Region, none other than his old crony, Colonel Michael Cassio, from the San Marx Military Academy.

Colonel Cassio—Mike to his friends—was a merry old soul, a true man-about-the-canal (he had his own gondola in Venice), charming with the ladies and an inexhaustible raconteur of after-dinner stories. In the months when Othello was wooing Desdemona, Mike Cassio had played Cupid by letting them have his own apartment for vows-making. But more important than all this, Cassio was a real Renaissance patriot.

With him on the quayside was Colonel Iago, a sour pusillanimous officer, who hated the Renaissance and all it stood for, being a secret agent of the Reincarnation Party. Iago bore a grudge against Cassio because this charming man had been appointed Deputy Commander, Cyprus Region, although his junior in years and length of service in the Army. Consequently, Colonel Iago had sworn by the Doge's head to wreak his revenge.

A propitious occasion arose at once. The same evening that the Othellos arrived, the happy population organized spontaneously, on Cassio's orders, a "Fiesta" for their new Governor. They gave him the full treatment, with fireworks, barrels of sweet Cyprus wine, and multi-coloured lanterns, and the revelry lasted into the small hours of the next morning. Huge banners were displayed everywhere with the inscription: "Long Live General Othello!", "Long Live the Renaissance!", "Ban the Powder!".

In the main square of the city was Colonel Cassio directing the public rejoicing. Iago went up to him with some 100 per cent proof alcohol and proposed several toasts to General Othello, Lady Desdemona and the Renaissance, which Iago loathed, and every time they drank a toast to this progressive movement, Iago surreptitiously emptied his glass into a nearby flower pot. Iago knew pretty well that Cassio was prone to get drunk easily because in his secret file it was written that even as a child he could not hold his liquorice.

Very soon Cassio became irremediably inebriated and was making merry with two local busybodies (women of easy virtue), called Nicosia and Famagusta, dutifully procured by Colonel Iago, who had also engaged a painter to paint Cassio in a compromising position. Then Cassio had a noisy brawl with an "agent provocateur", and when Lieutenant Montano, of the Military Police, tried to separate them, Cassio broke his pate, at which Montano uttered a piercing howl.

Aroused from his sleep, Othello jumped out of bed and rushed to investigate the cause of the clamour. He was distressed to discover that the big noise was none other than his friend, Colonel Michael Cassio, who had flagrantly violated military discipline and the two busybodies aided and abetted him in doing this. Othello accused him in legal jargon of "dipsomania acutis" and gave him a dishonourable discharge from the army. Othello was being lenient with him, because drunkenness with violence was punished in the Middle Ages by death by hangover, a cruel means of execution. The first part of Iago's revenge had come off.

Unemployed and desperate (the number of unemployed was particularly high in non-Socialist Cyprus), ex-Colonel Cassio approached Desdemona, again at Iago's instigation, and begged her to intercede in his favour with the General to have his commission restored. Kind Desdemona promised to do her best, and she did.

Othello lent a benevolent ear to her pleadings, because "Old Mike" was after all dear to his heart, yet he wanted to teach him a lesson, to impress upon him the serious character of his deviation, because for a man in the Renaissance Movement discipline was of paramount importance. But there in the background the despicable Iago was weaving his treasonable nest.

Once when General Othello arrived home and knocked on the front door to be let in by the wet-nurse, he noticed ex-Colonel Cassio leaving the house by the tradesmen's entrance. He thought at first that Cassio being short of money was plying some humble trade as a milkman or something similar, but he was rudely awakened from such innocuous suppositions by Iago who asked in a perfidious tone of voice: "And does Mike Cassio visit often Lady Desdemona?" adding for himself: "I do not like it!" Rather jokingly he advised Othello to be on his guard, "because nowadays, in our Middle Ages, with morals as they are, one cannot be too careful."

From that moment on, gone was "La Dolce Vita", the happy intercourse between Othello and Desdemona. As a first step, Othello ordered the tradesmen's entrance of his residence to be closed. He even nailed it up and that meant extra work for the wet-nurse who had to do the shopping herself and to walk long distances to the Cyprus Common Market (the ordinary people's shopping centre) for the various food items. As a protest this working woman staged a go-slow strike and took her time while shopping so that the schedule of Othello's meals was totally upset, which aggravated his black moods. When angry, General Othello used to roll his eyes in a menacing fashion.

Even his army career did not interest him any longer and he often gave the wrong command at military exercises. Utterly exasperated, he asked Iago to furnish him with some proof of his wife's infidelity. "Is it true that Lady Desdemona has a handkerchief spotted with strawberries?" asked cunningly the arch-plotter. "Perfectly true," replied Othello, "I gave it to her." "Well," said the reactionary Iago, "I saw ex-Colonel Cassio blowing his nose with the aforesaid handkerchief." "So there is some hanky-panky after all!" shouted Othello, rolling his eyes a couple of times, and he dashed off home to check the handkerchief story.

As soon as he entered the sitting room Othello sank into an armchair and began playing the detective. He

74

simulated a splitting headache and Desdemona, deeply concerned, offered a medieval remedy: "Would you like some of the fresh leeches that Mike Cassio brought the other day?" (Leeches were used for blood transfusions in the Middle Ages.) "And by the way," she added with a smile, "what about his commission?" "I want no bloody leeches!" shouted Othello (when angry he used to speak incorrectly, as foreigners often do). "Instead give me the handkerchief spotted with strawberries, you know the one, soak it in cold water and wrap it around my forehead!" "Keep your mail-shirt on!" (a soothing medieval expression), said Desdemona, offended by the tone of his voice and his incorrect speech, "I'll find it for you!" and she began to search for it in her drawers, but after turning them upside down she still could not find the handkerchief because a few days before, Emilia Iago the wife of the arch-plotter had called on her and when Desdemona had to go in the kitchen to prepare a special sauce, Mrs Iago had stolen it.

A few words here about Mrs Iago. Her husband besides being a reactionary in politics was also—as often happens with reactionaries—a spiritualist, that is, he sent table-grams to dead people and conversed with them. Mrs Iago herself was a medium and after her marriage had been a happy medium, but not for long.

Othello, seeing that Desdemona was searching in vain for the handkerchief said, "Aha," in an ominous tone of voice and left the house rolling his eyes.

Desdemona, deeply perturbed by this incident, thought at first that Othello might be jealous but knowing that there was no conceivable correspondent, dismissed the idea: "Perhaps he had bad tidings from Venice," she mused, "perhaps they cut the military aid!" Sighing, she got into bed for the "siesta" because in the afternoon the heat in Cyprus was intolerable and the streets were deserted.

Othello roamed the city for a while, drank several instant coffees (the waiters were very quick in Cyprus) and then set back home determined to kill his wife.

Entering the bedroom he saw Desdemona, "My Fair Lady" as he used to call her, prettier than ever in her sleep because she was dreaming that she was reconciled to Othello and they had a mixed-up kid (a multiracial baby). Othello shook her gently and said: "Wake up, Desdemona, and prepare for death. Name your last wish and you can eat anything you like!" Desdemona tried to appeal against the death sentence, protesting her innocence, but noticing that Othello was adamant she solemnly asked for a fair trial according to the principles of the Renaissance Movement. All was in vain. Rolling his eyes, Othello covered her up in the bedclothes and strangled her by the throat until she was dead.

After the execution, who should walk into the bedroom but Mike Cassio wounded and bleeding, wanting to know if Othello was engaged now in mass murders, because an attempt on his life had just been perpetrated by a scoundrel in Iago's pay. This scoundrel, in turn, is killed by Iago himself to prevent embarrassing disclosures, but in the pockets of the dead scoundrel are found letters proving the guilt of Iago and the innocence of Cassio. Othello noticing that he had been a poor judge of character, falls upon his sword and commits hara-kiri. The Cypriot homicide squad arrive on the scene and arrest Iago, who is hanged and then tried and sentenced, according to norms of progressive justice.

Now, in conclusion, a few words of literary guidance for Shakespearian scholars in the Soviet Union, to help them distinguish between the comedies and the tragedies of William Shakespeare. Shakespeare's comedies finish with a happy end, while the tragedies finish with murders, with a dead end. And so we reach, in this tragedy of Othello,

THE DEAD END

ARC BOOKS

ARE DESIGNED TO INSTRUCT AND ENTERTAIN. Each ARC BOOK is written by a top expert in his field.

Acting and Stage Movement (95¢)

Antique Furniture for the Smaller Home (95¢)

Archery (95¢)

The Art of Riding (95¢)

Astrology (95¢)

Boy or Girl—Names for Every Child (95¢)

Cheiro's Book of Numbers (95¢)

Cheiro's Palmistry for All (95¢)

Cheiro's When Were You Born (95¢)

Complete Guide to Palmistry (95¢)

Drama (95¢)

Fencing (95¢)

Health Foods and Herbs (95¢)

Heart Disease and High Blood Pressure (95¢)

How to Be Healthy with Yoga (95¢)

How to Train for Track and Field (95¢)

Judo and Self-Defense ($1.45)

Lawn Tennis (95¢)

Modern Statistics ($1.45)

Muscle Building for Beginners (95¢)

131 Magic Tricks for Amateurs (95¢)

Painting and Drawing (95¢)

Practical Guide to Antique Collecting (95¢)

Practice for Scholastic Aptitude Tests (95¢)

Production and Staging of Plays (95¢)

Public Speaking for Self-Improvement and Success ($1.45)

Radio Astronomy and Building a Telescope (95¢)

Sailing—Step by Step (95¢)

Slipped Discs (95¢)

Stamp Collecting for Fun and Profit ($1.45)

Stomach Ulcers (95¢)

The Student's Guide ($1.45)

Successful Wine Making at Home (95¢)

3 Great Classics ($1.45)

2300 Steps to Word Power ($1.45)

Upholstery (95¢)

Wake Up and Write (95¢)

Weight Lifting and Weight Training (95¢)

The Whole Truth About Allergy (95¢)

Woodturning (95¢)

ARC paperbacks are 95¢ each; ARC Giants are $1.45 each. Books are also available in cloth-bound library editions: ARC Cloth Books, $2.50; ARC Cloth Giants, $3.25.

If your bookstore is out of stock on any of the above titles, you can order books directly from ARC BOOKS, Inc., 219 Park Avenue South, New York, N.Y. 10003. Enclose check or money order for list price of books plus 10¢ per book for postage and handling. No C.O.D. Please specify "cloth" or "paper" edition.